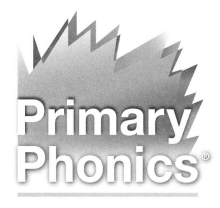

Primary Phonics®

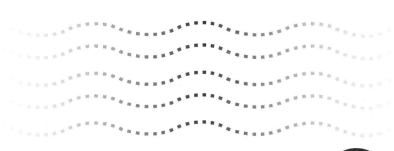

Comprehension Workbook 2

Thinking about Mac and Tab

EDUCATORS PUBLISHING SERVICE
Cambridge and Toronto

Thinking about Mac and Tab: Primary Phonics Comprehension

Text by Karen L. Smith

Illustrations by Anslie G. Philpot

Design by Persis Barron Levy

....

Educators Publishing Service, a division of School Specialty Publishing,
a member of the School Specialty Family.

Printed in USA

ISBN 978-0-8388-2382-8

21 22 PPG 22 21

Contents

Match.

vet

Mac

a pal

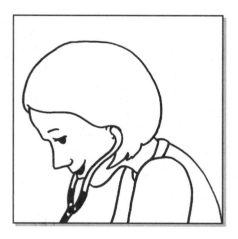

Circle yes or no.

Did the vet make Mac sit up?

Yes   **No**

Draw.

How is Tab on page 2?

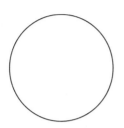

· ·

Draw or write.

How did Mac get well?

· ·

Circle the correct word to fill in the blank.

"Mac will get _____," said the vet.

nap   said   well

Match.

time to bat

not safe

home run

Circle yes or no.

Did Mike hit a home run on page 4?

Yes   **No**

Draw.

How was Mike at the end of the game?

            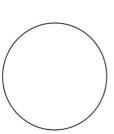

Draw or write.

What did Mike use to hit in the big game?

Circle the correct word to fill in the blank.

"I hope I get a _____," said Mike.

game   hit   home

Match.

Hal

Rafe fell in.

It is fun to wade.

Circle yes or no.

Did Rafe wade in the lake?

Yes   **No**

Draw.

How did Rafe like the joke?

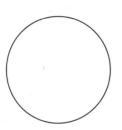

Draw or write.

What did Hal run to get?

Circle the correct word to fill in the blank.

Hal had fun in the _____.

bone   **lake**   **bike**

Match.

"I like cake," said Duke.

The cake fell on Duke.

Duke did not like cake on him.

Circle yes or no.

Did Pam run to get a hose?

Yes   **No**

Draw.

How did Duke like cake on his nose?

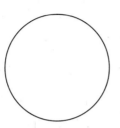

Draw or write.

How did Pam wipe up the mess?

Circle the correct word to fill in the blank.

The cake made a _____ on the tile.

home   **hose**   **mess**

Match.

The bee sat on a rose.

Lee came to a pie.

Lee sat on the doe.

Circle yes or no.

Was the doe a fine pal for Lee?

Yes   No

Draw.

Lee met a big bee. How was he?

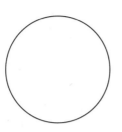

Draw or write.

Why did Pat not like the bee?

Circle the correct word to fill in the blank.

Lee and the big bee had a _____ time.

sad   **fine**   **like**

Match.

The goat ate a hole.

The goat ate soap.

The toad ran to hide.

Circle yes or no.

Did the goat run to the tub and dive in?

Yes   No

Under each box, write a number to show the correct order.

_____   _____   _____

Draw or write.

On page 6, who ran to hide?

Circle the correct word to fill in the blank.

The goat _____ up the road.

ate   **hid**   **ran**

Match.

The rain came.

Gail did bail.

Gail and Ben set sail.

Circle yes or no.

Did Gail and Ben get on Tim and ride home?

Yes   **No**

Under each box, write a number to show the correct order.

| "I see rain," said Gail. |  |  |

_____   _____   _____

Draw or write.

How did Gail and Ben get home?

Circle the correct word to fill in the blank.

The boat had a _____ hole in it.

big   **rain**   **cap**

Match.

Neal got a cod.

Neal got up on a seat.

The seal was not real.

Circle yes or no.

Did Neal the seal wave to Dean and Jean?

Yes   **No**

Under each box, write a number to show the correct order.

"This seal
seems sad,"
said Dean.

_____   _____   _____

Draw or write.

Who gave Jean and Dean a cute seal?

Circle the correct word to fill in the blank.

Neal got up on a _____.

seat   seal   nose

Match.

Joe ran up to the gate.

The big weed was home base.

"I can hide at the pole."

Circle yes or no.

Did Deb see feet at the gate?

Yes   **No**

Under each box, write a number to show the correct order.

"Did I win
the game?"
said Joe.

_____

_____

_____

Draw or write.

Where did Deb hide?

Circle the correct word to fill in the blank.

"I need to get _____ and take him home."

seen   **feet**   **Joe**

Match.

The deer ran in fear.

The hare ran to hide.

The rain came.

Circle yes or no.

Did Pete feel the heat of the fire?

Yes   **No**

Under each box, write a number to show the correct order.

"The rain made us safe," said Pete.		
_____	_____	_____

Draw or write.

How did the toad hide?

Circle the correct word to fill in the blank.

The man _____ a fine meal of ham and peas.

made   **was**   **hid**